Rerooted

Jackie Henrion

TURTLE
MOON
PUBLISHING

SANDPOINT, IDAHO

Cover photo: The Bonner County History Museum

Back Cover Photo Lake Pend Oreille: Dan C. Earle

Author Photo: Marie-Dominique Verdier - MDV Photography

Author Contact information: decouvrir@mac.com

Publisher Contact: Turtlemoonpub@gmail.com

ISBN-13: 978-1-7331672-0-8

Library of Congress Control Number: 2019907203

12-20-22

To Dagny

Here's to a budding friendship!

Jackie

It takes courage to get to the ancient altar

of the moment where I create individual time.

The picture body untremblingly stares large-eyed

I also create the tablets of exponential seeing: it brightens

all around it, as I'm the apparatus of what there is to be;

and I am making it, my time visibly becoming me.

Alice Notley
"Individual Time"

Jackie Henrion

The imprisonment which was at one and the same time understood as the imprisonment of the female mind has a larger boundary, and that is the shape of thought itself within Western civilization.

Susan Griffin
"Red Shoes"

... a "mistress narrative," you might say, perhaps preferable
subtle   persuasive
insistently oral
            most melodious tone

studied other languages on foreign language tapes
spent time in the prison library
an auspicious time
up against uncertain worlds
shrinking

where human is finite, an invention of recent date
time that we say our fantasies are controlled by propaganda
born too into the middle of a century before
  we are "gone"

 or when the mores changed and

favored women who were set up against each other in jealous
rage

that too passes... will pass

                                        Anne Waldman
                                        From *Gossamurmur*

Jackie Henrion

TABLE OF CONTENTS

Jackie Henrion

ACKNOWLEDGEMENTS

In addition to observations, sensations, and ideas, I reserve space in my journal for gratitude. This began several years ago while studying mindfulness with Leslie Villelli in Sandpoint Idaho. None of my creative projects would have been possible without her. The journal reminds me how a small puff of energy can significantly affect life's trajectory.

As I review these pages, it is my pleasure to acknowledge Kirpal Gordon, Christine Holbert and Suzy Prez whose original support helped me start along this path. I also honor the subsequent inclusive energy of Naropa's Mairead Case, J'Lyn Chapman, Hayes Moore, Jeffrey Pethybridge, Ambrose Bye and Giovannina Jobson.

I thank Dan Earle, my husband, whose love and support has been constant and immeasurable.

Anne Waldman has inspired me with the energy she devotes to a unique creative, intellectual, and spiritual program at Naropa. Her published work as author and editor is a portion of the ecosystem for this book.

The risks I've taken owe a great deal to the sparks from my classes with Kazim Ali, Laird Hunt and Eleni Sikelianos. Embodiment as a conceptual thread has its roots in a workshop with Sally Silvers and Bruce Andrews.

Gabrielle Civil has been a primary creative and intellectual impetus by introducing me to Gloria Anzaldúa's work and by her commitment to interaction with an audience.

I want to thank my Naropa mentor, Sara Veglahn, for recognizing the nascent form of the manuscript, and guiding me through its development.

Finally, I appreciate many others not mentioned here for their help in creating the space which made this work possible.

INTRODUCTION

This is a work of fiction. A number of names are based on real people, but their described activities are not factual. However, I believe the truth, like myth-making is a personal matter.

I mean to suggest that the whispers of women over time and space take on connective qualities. The apparently "empty space" is viscous with voices which echo against solid surfaces and equally solid belief systems. From this space/time, we experience the transpersonal: the epicenter of spirit. My writing, originating during the hours of dream work, resonates with the possibility in their voices.

TRANSFORMATION

A woman molts by the momentum of music. The symphony of possibility unfolds you in the space between conventional beliefs. The new skin on your face cannot stretch for one more feigned smile – you cannot mouth one more 'yes' when you mean 'no.' You refuse to clean the remains of one more mess or complete work for someone else. Your limbs move to a melody learned young, but increasingly out of tune. You will not prepare another meal to be left un-eaten. Rests become palpable and as necessary as air. Your own body's rhythms and temperatures require no excuse or explanation.

A careless comment has withered too many moments. You are aware that jealous rage or criticism is the creation of the other, no longer harmonic. You exit the domain of kidding, slaps, leather belts, thrown plates or glasses — metaphoric or real. A man's declarative voice loses its potency.

Your body no longer tolerates invasions of eyelashes, face, skin, lips, breasts, mouth, underarms and vagina. Your acquiescence to denigration is illuminated. Your voice, a crescendo declares, "I am tired of making myself small." This is the same moment when another's explanation of reality no longer suits you, names you, applies to you, makes sense to you, has power over you.

Perhaps this point feels desperate. Dangerous. Your mind is frozen – not able to face a turn, a dark corner, or unknown path. This anxiety may be short-lived or color many months, years or an entire lifetime. But at this very moment, a woman is a missile, ready to launch, with enough momentum to reach another reality – This woman has access to original energy.

Silence Then

Itwassocold

        Del'aubeclaire [In the early dawn]

        sevenyearsold

thisair

        Mybodybutwithin

        Bornhere

andfromitsdoors

            Idweltasifmyselfwereout

GREATER HOPE

G reater Hope adorns the north edge of Lake Pend Oreille in northern Idaho. Consisting of the areas known as Hope, East Hope, Hope Peninsula, The Highlands, The Cape of Art and Beyond Hope. Each of these names has its origin in a 150-year history of politics, property development, aesthetics and humor. In winter only a few hundred grey-skinned people hibernate here. The population in summer expands to over two thousand swimmers, boaters, fisherman, hikers, campers. But before the first European settlers, the original people migrated through from seacoast to plains to mountains, gathering here to exchange goods for thousands of years. Such names as Bannock, Kalispell, Kootenai, Coeur D'Alene are the names assigned to them. Before that, a megalithic ice dam between the mountains now called "Green Monarchs" and "Cabinets" unleashed immense floods over geophysical time. In a sense, Greater Hope is about transition, the moment between breathing in and out.

ARCHITECTURE

The architecture of a rose is Jenny's first art project at the Institute. Her subject: the apricot colored Honey Perfume Floribunda, the color of innocent and tumescent flesh, in her small garden. The life cycle of a rose unfolds over fourteen days from bud to bloom, then another fourteen days to death. A woman's cycle. She positions three 35-millimeter cameras, manually advancing only partial frames. One camera captures growth, the next, light, and the third she moves, choosing disparate views. The rose discloses secrets. One petal passing light to the next. In Jenny's frames, petals flow like liquid ice cream, softened, sliding, sloping. Her still photos inhabit the dimension of time.

I press my finger against a thorn to test its sharpness, wondering what evolutionary role it performs for such a beautiful thing. I recall a phrase from Marianne Moore's "Roses Only:"

You do not seem to realize that beauty is a liability rather than an asset - that in view of the fact that spirit creates form, we are

justified in supposing

that you must have brains.

POSSIBLE

lookingoverourheads

Onefootofthesun

hadjustcrossed

        thepowerofyourintensefragility

anditdoesmoretothat

incrediblejusticeandlikeness

        alongwiththesun

Hematite

Hematite is a compound of two elements: Iron and Oxygen. Iron oxides are visible in stones and metal as rust, and the red color, called ochre, was used in earliest human writing and art. Hematite forms an ancient and elemental crystal which is sensitive to the earth's magnetic fields. Used in needle of a compass, it points north. In a 1992 study at CalTech, hematite was found to be present in biological cells in minute quantities, nonetheless strongly sensitive to magnetic forces. Hematite is present in the brains of migrating birds and other mammals. It allows them to sense the direction of North and South.

Do women still have access to this directional sense? Or have we ignored it for too long?

SALOON OF HOTEL HOPE

The Saloon of the Hotel Hope offers respite for my husband and me. We have been looking for property on which to build a home. The bar of the hotel seems to be a restoration of what would have been a Saloon in the days when old growth white pine was money and when men were clear-cutting forests, balancing on log jams on the Clark Fork River, feeding massive tree trunks into the maws of saws, mining lime and sundry other non-precious metals, hunting deer, elk, bear, or fishing the Lake Pend Oreille sturgeon to extinction.

As I walk into the Saloon, however, my attention is drawn towards the back of the long room to see a reclining nude woman in stained glass, mounted to observe the activities and the spectacular lake view.

I appreciate her proprietary air. I have no idea who she is, but the back of the menu offers a short explanation: the stained-glass odalisque is an artist's rendition of the former owner, Marie Root, installed after her death. Is it possible that her DNA is in the dust particles accumulating on the edges of the mirror ledges? Does the carved wood bar and wall paneling resonate with her vibration – like a phorminx, still attuned to the hand of a muse? I sense why religions warn against graven images. There is a concentration of force in certain pictures; an intimacy, which radiates energy and accepts all projections. At this moment my projections are Delphic.

TREE POSE

I am working to improve my Tree Pose, or Vrksasana. Even though I press down into the standing leg, my balance remains unsteady. One day I look in the mirror, becoming aware that the position of my head stays centered as if it is still in Mountain pose, halfway between each foot. Struggle, failure and ungraceful exit from this position has been common. Doing this against a wall to remain balanced is even more common.

In an effort to try something different. I shift my head so that it is directly over my right foot. This shift allows me to lift my other leg more easily to place my foot on the inside upper thigh. The ease surprises me. My shoulders become less tense. My breath, more natural. My foot does its job, with the slightest of adjustments. I feel rooted to the earth as the energy in my hip presses down and up into my ribcage at the same time.

My hands move from supplication towards the sky, towards the light. My stability is now only measured by the tension in my supporting calf. The right place, for the first time.

Afterwards, I note that awareness in life comes in similar shifts. Something which causes frustration and imbalance can be altered by small adjustments. Easy and difficult at the same time.

Jackie Henrion

Mary Davis Arrives in Hope

Twenty-one-year-old Mary Davis arrives in Hope on the Northern Pacific Railroad, along with Clinton Root. She nimbly descends the iron steps lifting the hem of the green linen dress she had stitched by hand. The dress is tightly cinched at the waist, the elegance not diminished by wrinkles even after the eight-day journey. A number of men take notice of her from the windows of the ten bars which overlook the station. They remark on her auburn hair against the green bonnet. As she trips over a loose board, their bodies spring slightly forward as if to catch her, even as she recovers with graceful ease. In their alcoholic haze they imagine themselves either heroes or seducers.

Mary is introduced as Marie, Clinton's new bride. The Root family is surprised to see them, without any notice. They are even more surprised that Clinton, their nephew, unable to carry or cut any lumber worth using, whom they remember from Michigan, as a feckless girl chaser, had managed to marry a woman who is both comely and intelligent.

They do not know he helped her escape from an alcoholic husband who intermittently harassed, beat, threatened, abused, and intimidated her for the previous six years. She has left her son behind, knowing that if she had taken him, her husband would have hunted her like prey. A savage ransom. A note tucked into a pocket, "I am leaving the two I love the most," a diversionary despair, hoping he will think she has taken her own life. In a way, she has. Periodically fear freezes her body, her gaze becomes distant, distracted. This state arouses the men and arouses suspicion in the women of the town.

She avoids all discussion of her past as Mary, so the news of her arrival does not get back to Mt. Pleasant, which was anything but.

Jackie Henrion

DER HEILIGE SKARABÄUS

Else Jerusalem's 600-page documentary novel is published under the title Der Heilige Skarabäus (The Holy Scarabeus). The industrious dung beetle as a metaphor. The book is re-published numerous times in Europe and is widely read there. The protagonist, Milada, is raised in a brothel. However, she evolves, prevails and transcends.

Jerusalem, a student of philosophy, a spirited intellectual, and advocate of women's rights, alludes to the scarab, an ancient icon of pre-Christian beliefs. The scarab is the original symbol of 'Maat,' the Egyptian feminine universal ordering system of balance and justice. Male Pharaohs of Egypt assiduously eradicated all artifacts of the long and peaceful reigns of the female rulers.

The use of the Latin term Scarabeus refers to the beetle genus, which resolutely rolls dung balls, guided by magnetic sensitivity, to the nest. Therein the female lays her eggs which eat the dung for food when they emerge: a metaphor for the source of eternal creation from the "dung" of the world. Was she also referring to the scarab as a symbol of the female sexual organ?

DIARY

Dear Niswi

I may never feel your body again, but the shape of it is carved into my own enduringly. I will write this note, even though it will never be mailed, for I know not where you are, and so it becomes the first page in my journal. Last year, when you said you were going to leave your home I didn't realize that your absence would make my own life insufferable. My beautiful boy, W— died sadly, and R— continued his descent, as you had predicted. His only solace is our last son.

On this train my body feels collapsed, as if all bones dissolved in the volcanic heat of R— 's anger. But my skull bumping against this train window, as the scenery flickers past, reminds me of something so familiar and lost, like our heads softly bumping against each other as your mother carried us on her back. I am sitting backwards, watching the green hills and pine trees disappear, much as they did then. Going away from, yet ever present. The past seems so much more real than any future I can now imagine.

Clinton helped me escape from my torturous situation. He has even tried to cheer me a bit by buying me this small diary as a gift. This journal ignites my thoughts of you, of leaving my son, and the fear of every corner and shadow. Do you remember the notes we left for each other in tree stumps, bushes and cairns? Like those, your name on the top of each page will give me fortitude. You will understand that it is even difficult to write full names in these letters. Even my name is new, so I will not be recognized through letters to Clinton's family back home.

Yours alone, Marie

Jackie Henrion

AN ECHO

The first time I see her, the sun silhouettes her form with the grace of a dancer. She sits in the hotel saloon. After a few minutes she looks up at me with a small in-breath of recognition. No shock or disapproval of my nakedness or pose (both survey and seduction) while she absorbs my place in this place. A trim woman, with greying hair which flips around a face with a hint of Eurasian ancestry and perhaps some Celtic. She moves easily, an awareness like conversation in her limbs. A man companion sits nearby, in the old-fashioned sense, you might say, with the build and gait of a warrior. Laughing easily, her teeth have character, as teeth were wont to in my time.

In my time – Ah, time – that is something I know of now. Despite over a half century from my passing, my presence still resonates within this room, this hotel, this town, this lake, these mountains, this country. As I watch her, I notice that she senses me. The first one to do so. Her eyes slowly scan around the surfaces of the bar mirror and carved wooden features as if she knows that the particles which appear as dust manifest my energy still: the darkened heart pine reflects the touch of my fingers, the pressure of my torso. The grand mirror echoes my humming as I cleaned and polished with the vigor of full bloom.

She takes out a pad of paper and begins to write! I can barely contain myself. Even though, no longer having a self, I don't know what that means -- does the air glow somehow from my excitement? Do harmonic tones resonate with the bar glasses? Do the trees outside the picture windows shake, even as the sun reflects on the lake. She has the spirit, but does she have the stamina?

History of Mary Davis

I am delving into the history of Mary Davis. She was the fifth child of Aaron and Mary in 1887, and I see that a girl born the next year does not survive infancy. I wonder if her mother has started to have childbirth difficulties? Not unlike my own mother who was unable to care for me right after birth. I wonder who cared for her, since there was no immediate family living nearby, not even a grandmother like mine. But the land which surrounded their farm consisted of many plats awarded to the native Ojibwa tribe by a settlement agreement. It is not inconceivable that her mother knew a Native American woman who was able to nurse and care for her, since the tasks on a frontier farm and caring for four other young toddlers could have been overwhelming.

I see also that Mary married in 1902. How does one marry at 15? It might have started one day in church when she noticed Robert staring at her. Her father insists that the entire family attends services, since he is on the Advisory Board and is keen to maintain his standing within the small community. At first, she blushes at the intensely focused stare. Then her eyes dart back to notice that he is a tall, slender, handsome man, with dark hair and a dark complexion, but strange blue eyes. Her cheeks flush pink and she freezes to stillness when she notices him. After several weeks of the same intense gaze, he says hello, introduces himself and walks alongside her as they leave the service. He ventures a few observations about the weather, asks her name, and enquires about the other members of her family who usually sit next to her in the pew. He asks if she goes to school to which she replies, "Oh yes, I enjoy school very much." Not wanting to boast about how quick she is to learn and how she has read ahead in most of her studies, she doesn't say, "They sometimes ask me to teach the younger ones." She doesn't say she also teaches her Ojibwa friend Niswi.

Niswi had been taken in by Mary's family when all the other Ojibwa children were taken to live at the Government school. This might have been in gratitude or it may have been that the girls had become so close at this point, Mary had begged her mother to consider it.

It might also have happened that Robert approached Mary's father, Aaron, to ask about the possibility of marriage. Aaron must have consented, since Robert was a good member of the church. But Niswi would have been the one to see that being a member of the church had nothing to do with being a good human. It may have been Niswi who said, "This man is not on a good path - his center is not aligned with earth spirit - his heart and words do not work together." But Mary doesn't understand and still flushes at the thought of his intense gaze. It gives her a little thrill to think herself the target of his attention. It is no less of a thrill than her friendship with Niswi, just different.

The day of her marriage, two months later, is the best and worst of her life.

VIEW

Mary Davis is born in Isabella County, Michigan, near Lake Huron. The fifth child of Aaron and Mary Davis who had carved their farmland from Native American allotments sold off by the Ojibwa who could no longer survive in their traditional ways. The mother is so ill from childbirth that she beseeches her Ojibwa housekeeper and friend to wet-nurse and care for the child along with her own daughter born three months prior. The mother fashions a double *dikkinagun,* a cradle board, which secures the two infants together for almost the entire first year of their lives. After six months their arms are left outside the swaddling and they explore each other and interact constantly. Mary's first sounds mimic the native language. At two years old, the young Ojibwa girl receives the name Niswi Manitou (Three Spirit). Her spirit is not clearly girl or boy, but rather another one, who sees from many views.

The cradle board for the two infants, carried on the mother's back, affects an infant's relationship with time: the past reassures even as it recedes. The future arrives as it will, without expectations, without anxiety. The true test of courage and faith is to fall into the future, with one's back turned.

Jackie Henrion

Transition

Mary's eyelids flicker open as the rising sun floods into her bedroom window. The white curtain a scrim, where shadows of white pine branches dance. Robert snores noisily, the alcohol on his breath reaching her in nauseating puffs. The pine boards which panel the ceiling are patterned with elliptical forms, each spinning on a slightly different axis. This morning she knows, looking up, that this will be a different day. All the whispering, plans, saving, tickets, packing, hoarding, are hurtling her toward a new world. There is no more fear. This morning there is only residual pain from the abuses of last night. The pain eclipses, it overcomes, it drives. A spontaneous momentum propels her limbs.

She rises quietly out of bed and tiptoes into the room where little Andrew sleeps. At the age of barely one year, she can already see the resemblance to Robert; dark hair, heavy brow, softened only by the fat still left in his cheeks. Trancelike, she steps to his cabinet to choose his clothes carefully; noting the trousers she hand-sewed against the blue cotton shirt suitable for church. Robert will be proud of his son this morning. The only survivor of three children. Robert will hold him tightly to soften his own demeanor in the eyes of the other parishioners. It will be convincing. Especially since her own father will walk over to beam proudly at his grandson. The parishioners will cluck over little Andrew, "Why Aaron Davis, you sure know how to make handsome grandkids." Aaron will wink at Robert, just like men do, who conspire to contribute so little to conception and all that follows but bask in the credit.

Just after the service, Mary excuses herself from the

gathering and food, saying, "I have to make a run to the schoolhouse to prepare the exams for the final tests tomorrow. I'll meet you at home later this afternoon." Robert raises an eyebrow in concern as he did whenever she excuses herself from his presence, but today, she doesn't reassure him with a smile. She simply turns away as if her attention were diverted. She walks out of the yellow clapboard church building briskly toward the school. It takes her only fifteen minutes to get to Clinton's house, going around to the side and tapping Beethoven's fifth on his window pane lightly. He comes to the window, without a stitch of clothing, and the residue of morning still apparent. When she doesn't smile he knows this day is different. His look questions, her nod a reply. Fifteen minutes later he approaches quietly, carrying a heavy leather suitcase.

He whispers: "I'll go get the mule and cart and we'll pick up your suitcase at the school. We should be able to make it by noon without any problem."

But there was a problem. The suitcase was there, but the canister where Mary had been saving her money for years, had apparently been found. She had secreted pennies, nickels, dimes which grew to the sum of 64 dollars and 24 cents. Now only one errant penny lay on the ground next to the canister cover. Mary is shocked into silence. Then says, "I can't believe it - it's gone." Her head starts to pound like a sharp nail being driven into the center of it.

Clinton extends his arm around her shoulder, leads her away from the street to the back of the school where no one can see them. He slides his other arm around her, holding her to him, rocking side to side trying to console her.

"Take it easy, Mary, let's just think for a moment." She groans into his chest, "If Robert even suspects this, he'll imprison me or worse!"

Jackie Henrion

Clinton says, "Ok, ok, calm yourself. I have an idea. Don't you have a collection box in the school cabinet?

Mary gasps, "My God, Clinton, that's for the end of the year school trip! What are you thinking?"

Clinton says, "Look, Mary, there is something about you this morning which tells me we will never return here. When it comes to survival, everyone can justify throwing rocks at windows. Tell me where the key is, and I'll get into the cabinet."

Mary describes the location of the key and with his usual brash confidence, he finds the school cash box and removes forty-five of the seventy-two dollars in the box.

He says, "Well, I left them enough for a good picnic instead."

They load their suitcases on to the cart and he whips the donkey into a fast caper toward the train station. They arrive twenty minutes prior to the arrival of the noon train. While Clinton pays a young man to get the rig back to his house, Mary buys two tickets for Hope, Idaho on the Northern Pacific Rail Road. She asks if they have any more information about the town. The ticket salesman says, "Why yes, the company just printed this little information sheet about Hope Idaho, which they call the Alpine Lake of the Northwest Territory. You know, they made a brand-new state out there called Idaho. And a woman designed the state seal. Imagine that!"

THREE MONTHS APART

We were born only three months apart, and became friends just like our mothers, but different. Different experiences, different intelligences, both brilliant like water drops on a petal. Our shared childhoods were resonant with parks, streets, horns and machinery of the greatest, grittiest city. Our limbs entwined on monkey bars, swings, slides, sandboxes and school. Our friendship was not filial, more like competition for sunlight, more like moss in different niches. Making pigment from ground stones of differing colors, from blood red to pale green. Making ice cream sodas in root beer, I wonder "What makes the heavy ice cream float and fizz?" Concocting mad monopoly games, because Jenny doesn't believe in conventions or rules — at least for games. Playing a game of jacks beneath a grand piano. The same grand piano where her new father arranges songs for Peter, Paul and Mary, the Brothers Four, Chad Mitchell Trio and John Denver. She will not know that my diary pages all begin with "Dear Jenny."

GUY AND HELEN

I face north in Jenny's garden near Notting Hill Gate, London. On a 'great circle' 4,484 miles to my left, at that same moment, I would be in northern Idaho. There, Guy and Helen Neyman are just waking up on the second-floor bedroom suite at the Hotel Hope. After three years of renovation they had mounted the finishing touch in the Saloon the night before. They are excited about going down to see it in the morning light. The chilly air reminds Helen of Christmas, although the view from the window is lit with the bright yellow maple leaves still clinging to the branches of trees across the narrow road in front of the hotel. Miles away, across Lake Pend Oreille, the luminescent sunlight-colored larches light up the steep slopes of the Green Monarchs. In their robes, Helen and Guy descend the newly carpeted steps. At the bottom, Helen says, "Wait, I want to turn on the lights," and reaches around the dark wood molding to flip the switch in the bar.

As they turn the corner, Guy slips his arm around Helen's waist and both slowly look over the renovated room. Their mouths form an unspoken "wow" and they shake their heads, not quite believing the transformation. The dark heart pine woodwork radiates warmth. Glasses and bottles, arrayed on shelves, are mounted on a huge mirror behind the massive bar on the right. There, in the mirror, is the reflection of last night's work. A stained-glass odalisque mounted at the back of the room, just below the stamped metal ceiling. Reclining, the nearly-nude woman surveys the large space, looking out towards the lake through the large window panes at the front of the hotel bar. The glass, lit from behind, gives her flesh a palpable, eerie accuracy. She leans on her right arm, on a carved Grecian style divan. Draped with the impression of lush forest-green fabric, two aspects nod to modesty: a fold of fabric and a discretely placed garland of violet roses beneath her breasts. An artistic arrangement of rare blue glass segments creates a background which might be water or sky. But how did the artist capture the face? The equanimity of a Madonna, a Magdalene, a matriarch, a mender, and a mystery, seeming to say, "No human behavior is alien."

MAGNETIC NORTH

Magnetic North is not "True North." The word 'true' is misleading. It does not mean true as in truth; rather, it is a term that allows all of us to use the concept "north" as a 'truing-up device" for all of our little human concerns. By this we are able to make maps, to navigate, to delineate property, to meet at the right place and give directions to others. In other words, True North is an agreed upon, useful geographical term. As long as maps have been made, they have been marked with variegated Compass Roses to denote the difference between True and Magnetic North.

The term "True North" is necessary because magnetic north changes. It drifts. Not only does it change over time, it changes depending on location. The formal term for this is declination, or deviation, usually symbolized by the Greek letter delta: δ. This difference can vary up to 16 degrees west in Maine or close to 0 degrees in London. The magnetic patterns of the earth may even flip, based on the flux of the liquid-like flows of iron in the earth's core. The core is in constant flux and is also sensitive to 'sun-burps,' as radiation hurtles towards and through the earth from the sun and other gravitational entities in our solar system. In addition, the magnetic readings may be inaccurate if there are nearby metal ships or deposits of iron ore.

Modern navigation depends on the skill of translating and verification from positions of entities in the solar system. But even stars change. Though the rate of stellar change is hardly discernible for most purposes, except for space travel.

The history of navigation is as old as human history. The most recent, European understanding was codified by the self-educated American genius Nathanial Bowditch in his 1802 book *The New American Practical Navigator*.

But here's where men go astray. They forget True North is a "constructed concept." They believe that it is an absolute truth.

Women have a different view. Perhaps due to the sensation of magnetic hematite ~ perhaps mutability has its own beauty ~ perhaps time threads more intimately in a woman's body ~ perhaps because water smooths even stone ~ they have a different way of knowing 'True.'

Jackie Henrion

BEYOND HOPE

Dear Niswi,

I am afraid we will be forced to move west. This town of Hope is so small we've become acquainted with all the residents but are unable to find honest employment. Clinton is not suited to work in the mills, having neither the strength or temperament. Even the new mill, in East Hope where his relatives work, is no longer welcoming. Nor has he capability or inclination for mining or fishing.

What seems to suit him is socializing at the saloons. So much so, in fact, that the owner of the Hotel has invited him to play cards and work with the house to ensure that the winnings do not "walk out the door." His charm extends to both women and men and some nights he doesn't return. The only work I've been able to find is a few odd seamstress jobs for the women who work there. They are beginning to trust me with more mending for their torn dresses, which they say is a "professional hazard."

We live in a single room with a cast iron firebox and I must pay to have buckets of water hauled to our barrel inside the room to avoid freezing. The town is set into a mountain of layered rock which descends into the lake, so soil must be hauled from the upland forests, making gardens unyielding. Perhaps it is ironic that I am bereft of hope here in Hope. I feel like I am walking in a daze. My mind, an inescapable maze. My body as heavy as stone that, with a slight stumble, threatens to tumble into the frigid lake water. My petrified body signals that every choice I have made in my life is wrong. I can't remember the last time I laughed. I imagine it was with you — almost ten years ago.

Your Marie

DULCE ROSA

Richard sends me a draft of his opera libretto for *Dulce Rosa*. No, that's not true - his wife, Jenny, sends it and asks,

"What do you think?"

I say, "I enjoyed it, except the part where the woman jumps in front of the bullet aimed at the man who raped her, thereby sacrificing her life for his, because she loves him."

I ask Richard, "Why does the woman have to die, why not the man?"

He writes back, "Because that's how Isabel Allende's story goes, and besides, it's a classic tragic ending."

Reading the Allende story titled *Una Venganza* (A Revenge), my reaction is the same. It would be just as tragic if the man had died. Richard's feelings are hurt by my comment, so he asks Jenny not to send his drafts to me again.

Meanwhile Jenny and Richard travel to England, Mexico, Bolivia, and Venezuela to photograph roses: in gardens, on buildings, on villas, on trellises, on bodices. She works with a young set designer to develop new technologies to combine and project images for the LA Opera company. Although she now creates her collaged structures with computer technology, the current challenges involve managing light so that images are sufficiently saturated, consistent with the stage set, and not blocked by the figures on the stage. Her journals/letters are delightful mind-maps.

Jackie Henrion

THREE BOYS

Just after 4:30, when dusk is pinking the snow-dusted Green Monarchs, three boys stride into the Hope Hotel Bar with smirks on their faces. Marie raises her eyebrows and asks from behind the bar,

"What can I do for you young men?"

The second one shoves the first, "Tell her."

The first boy says, "We want a woman - and we can pay!"

Marie cocks her head to the side and looks them over. A smile stretches her lips,

"And how old are you, now?"

The third boy pipes up "Eighteen, for sure!"

She thinks for a moment about the apparent lie, but then says,

"And how much are you prepared to pay?"

The first one puffs out his chest, "Twenty dollars."

Marie's eyes widen in amusement since that means quite a bit for boys who probably didn't earn more than $1.25 per hour for any labor they'd be capable of.

She says, "You're too young, but for that same price I will show you a dance that will remain in your memories until you are over 90 and too old to remember where you put your teeth."

The second boy whines, "Awww."

But the first boy is committed to having some kind of adventure he can boast about. He elbows the second boy and looks over at the third with a question. The third boy gives a quick nod, which is seconded by the other.

She says with a wink, "Nathan can you take over the bar for a while, we have a few customers."

"Sure thing, Mrs. Root."

She leads the three boys up to the parlor, settles them into the divans and after taking up the fee, goes off to change. She returns, wrapped in a series of veils and starts the record player. She asks the boys, "Have you ever heard of Bing Crosby? I'll tell you a little secret, he's a friend of mine from Spokane and he gave me a record of some of his songs."

After positioning the Victrola's needle, she faces them, and for the next 30 minutes she twists, turns, unveils and burns her way into their memories to the most provocative music of the day. At the end, her skin is flushed and damp. The boys stand at attention. She bends over, closely. Scent and musk waft around them. To each, she offers a preserved rose from her collection.

STOCKHOLM SYNDROME

Placido Domingo conducts the premier of Richard's *Dulce Rosa* with the LA opera. The title means "Sweet Rose." In her introduction that evening, Isabel Allende explains the plot in her story by citing the Stockholm Syndrome, defined as "strong emotional ties that develop between two persons where one person intermittently harasses, beats, threatens, abuses, or intimidates the other." The term was coined in 1973 by criminologist and psychiatrist Nils Bejerot to describe the peculiar reaction observed in hostages during a Swedish bank robbery.

Although only recently recognized, this frame of mind appears to be endemic to women throughout history to current time. Cognitive linguist George Lakoff suggests that we interpret reality by such metaphors. How many women reject partners and candidates because they are "too nice"?

MIND-KEEPERS

I worked for twenty years in purchasing roles in large manu-facturing companies, where men are Mind-Keepers. A hostage learns to create an alternate identity, attuned to jokes, feeding hab-its, drinking habits, chains of command. A hostage learns a lan-guage of nonverbal clues: voice tone, leaning in, leaning away, and humor, always humor. One Mind-Keeper named Carl, retired Navy, crew cut, short, body weight disproportionate, tells jokes for more hours than he works. That's a good thing. A necessary thing. A life line for hostages. The official definition of the Stockholm Syndrome affecting hostages lacks the recognition of subtlety: the subtlety of silence, of eagerness, of benign disaffection, of anger's threat, of estrangement. But there is also gratitude, for ultimately if we sur-vive such estrangement, we reach the space in-between, we come to know ourselves.

Estrangement is dis-integration. You look in the mirror wondering 'who is she?' Words come from your mouth without connection to gut, heart, the dark folds of your brain. At work you use the language of others instead of your own. The separation has its costs. An unacknowledged nervous tension blocks digestion, blocks hunger, blocks thirst, causing you to say things you don't believe, causing you to believe things you can never say. Eventually either something breaks, or something changes. Only then can the body search for healing modes: meditation, yoga, exercise, healthy food, water, water, water.

Finally, when self-care heals, you re-integrate. Lies are a waste of energy. Your body's truth becomes evident. You shed the artifacts: makeup, jewelry, clothing, perfume, and products of a culture not yours. You realize you have been tested ~ you have tested yourself ~ and you have survived. You give birth to yourself. Unrecognizable to many.

WORKING

foraminutealone

                              Iamlarge

workingthestone

alongtheriver

                              mysoul

Infront

mymansionmadeforme

Jackie Henrion

GREENWICH VILLAGE

W e survive our childhoods. By a miracle. We were lucky, both strange at a young age. Perhaps because of parents whose instabilities were obscured by artistry. Her Mother, a perfect distillation of the anxious disorders of an Irish Catholic ancestry and her birth Father, well, simply crazy in the way a man is crazy in his childhood skin for too long. Always fighting against an imagined authority, never really becoming. The other Mother, dazed by shock of unexpected parenthood and the vestige of Jewish parents horrified by the possibility of a Catholic son-in-law, whose anger is embedded in genes altered by alcohol.

Control or neglect. Both meet at the violet space in the spectrum of floral possibilities. Both parenting styles provide rich soil, from which we grow. One over-concerned about safety and sin, the other, sinning of no concern. A sibling might use the word neglect, but after all, the Mothers changed every single shitty diaper. The irrevocability of that scene shrouds my own attempts at childbearing. Nonetheless, the education and exposure of New York City enliven both Jenny and I, even as we play in the sandbox at Washington Square Park where the first sounds we hear are pigeons and folk music.

INTERVIEW WITH LING DAO, LAWYER

Q: How did you know Marie Root, the owner of the Hotel Hope?

A: She was my client beginning in 1961. She moved to Spokane in 1962. I dealt mostly about matters related to her estate, which included the Hotel Hope located in Hope, Idaho.

Q: How did she choose you as her lawyer?

A: One of my long-term clients was Lui Den who was a very close friend of hers when he lived in Hope and afterwards. He recommended me, and she trusted his judgment.

Q: What was your impression of her?

A: She was a very formal lady. But she was also very clear about what she wanted and expressed herself very strongly. A noble demeanor, accustomed to being in charge. I believe her age to be close to 80 when she came to see me, but she still dressed elegantly, almost, if I might say, vainly. She wore a minimum of jewelry, but always the same pendant and brooch every time I saw her. No wedding ring on her immaculately manicured hands.

Q: What did you do for her?

A: At first, I merely prepared an inventory of the estate, which included a great many personal items as well as the real estate she owned in Hope.

Q: Is it possible to see the inventory?

Jackie Henrion

A: I can't show that to you as a matter of professional ethics, but I believe the current owner has a copy and you could certainly ask him.

Q: How long did she use your services?

A: I worked for the estate until after her death in 1968, until I had sold the assets to Mr. and Mrs. Neyman from California and donated a number of assets as directed in her will. The new owners asked a few questions, about her legal directive about non-disclosure until 50 years after her death. They apparently wanted to create some new art for the hotel. I advised them that the restriction applied to documents specifically from the estate, not any new work.

Q: What is your overall memory of her?

A: Well to be frank I developed a fondness for her. There were many white lawyers in Spokane and my usual clients were Chinese, but she chose to work with me nonetheless. She had a quality of ... em, perhaps it could be called respect, a kind of intimate respect. I felt as if she were gathering all those who surrounded her in a ... kind of cradle or net ... like safe, ... like home. I remember her as pleasant and sometimes quite funny.

Q: What do you mean by funny?

A: She had a talent for mimicry and could also drop from an elegant demeanor to coarse language. She was very popular at parties, when she had the energy to attend.

Q: Did you know about the full extent of the activities at the Hotel?

A: Initially, I didn't, but then, as we reviewed the financial information I asked her how it was possible to have accumulated such a level of savings and she was completely open about what she called "Hospitality Services."

Paris

Alexandre Dumas *fils* wants to impress his father. He writes a novel modeled on his brief affair with the young, enchanting Madam Duplessis. In his novel, Violetta, a charming bacchanalian, throws raucous Parisian parties, wears a red camellia on her dress when she is menstruating and a white one, when she is not. Thus, his title *La Dame Aux Camellias*. Violetta dies of consumption after sacrificing her love for the honor of her lover's family. The real-life Madame Duplessis also dies at the age of 23, after a brilliant seven-year career as a Courtesan, admired for her charm, wit, intelligence and skill. Hundreds attend her funeral.

Jackie Henrion

History of the Courtesan

The history of the Courtesan in France is literary and potent. Courtesan was a role made possible by a combination of physical beauty, intelligence, education in liberal arts. Respect was earned by knowledge of philosophy, music, art, poetry and notable other skills such as horseback riding. Sexual prowess was a requisite skill, but in a nuanced way which inspired love and admiration long after an intimate relationship ceased. Often Courtesans had sources of money independent from their benefactors. But above all, they were creative about politics and life, which required a different way of knowing how to construct reality at every moment; how to weigh subtle signals and human nature to their advantage. It allowed such women a unique level of independence and power. In a sense, the status traded the safety of marriage for freedom and independence not generally available to women in the 16th to the 19th century.

VOLITION

everyatomofmyblood

thatwasgoing

tobeserved

Atsixo'clock

Iharborforgoodorbad

Verywellthen

Iamthecaptainofmysoul

Jackie Henrion

Marquise de Chatelet

In the humid inferno of a summer day, Marquise de Chatelet invites Voltaire to stay at her castle. Her childhood was enriched with an early and extensive education in the classics. She hosts numerous salons and studies with scientists and philosophers of the day. According to the scholar Judith Zinsser, her essays included science and energy discussions such as: *Dissertation Sur la Nature et la Propagation du Feu* (On the Nature and Propagation of Fire), *Discours Sur le Bonheur* (Discourse on Happiness), a French translation of passages of the Old and New Testaments, Mandeville's *Fable of The Bees*, as well as optics, liberty and grammar. She and Voltaire become lovers and collaborators during which time they review 20,000 books and set up a laboratory to do numerous experiments until her death in 1749. She shares her scientific and philosophical thoughts, which oppose Locke and Hobbes, and are ultimately appropriated by the philosopher Emmanuel Kant. She translates Sir Isaac Newton's *Principia* from Latin to French, making it more widely available. Despite her sponsorship, Voltaire gives up on attempts to write about science, returns to literature and philosophy and subsequently publishes his greatest works after her death.

WORKING WOMAN

I work to distinguish woman words

Separate but hungry, a different

red light

Bits of productive pond stems rise, chests

knitted baby socks

the gift of seeing unknown

The reward a blue haired queen, into

the world from lakes

speaking essence dutifully

plucking every bucket

from hard living beneath the self's pleasure

The cedar leaves, strewn to sculptures

in intimate places, say love

was cumbersome like a fading corona

Although the night, a shimmering winter reality

as woods sink to a highly colored spectrum

We would grow flowers there first

Jackie Henrion

MYTH

After our house on the Hope Peninsula is completed, I stop at the Hotel to talk to the current owner who frequently sits at the end of the bar at the Saloon, looking out towards Lake Pend Oreille. I ask him about the paperwork that came with the hotel. He said he had a register with quite a number of well-known people. Some of them used pseudonyms, but with a little research, you could decipher their identity. I asked if there was anything else. He said he had a box of miscellaneous paperwork, but nothing of any real value. I asked if I could see the contents of the box. He asked why, and I told him I was writing a song about the woman portrayed in the stained glass.

"Ah - she is the myth!" He said, "Let me think about it. Come back next week." By the time I went back I had thought of all kinds of persuasive things to say. He wasn't there, but the barkeep, said, "I have a box for you. But you have to look at it here, you can't take it outside the building." I calmed my excitement and said, "Great, I'll take a look." About twice the size of a shoebox, it was filled mostly with sheaves of accounting books, held together with a green ribbon. But beneath that were journals and loose pages. I spent the entire day leafing through the journal pages; a series of letters, apparently unsent.

ACTING

Dear Niswi,

I must say that the most difficult part of this whole business is hiring women. The only way it is palatable is by taking the view which Lui recommended, which is to think of them like xiaojie, or entertainers, actresses or maids in waiting. So, I have changed my recruiting questions. I still go to the houses in San Francisco and Seattle and one in Spokane, but now I am thinking differently. I look for women who are more interested in expanding their options and their lives. I have had much more success when they are interested in learning other useful things like reading, sewing, cooking, housekeeping, and even accounting for the clever ones. This presents the risk that an unmarried man will fall in love with such a woman. It seems to work best that we have a three-year contract during which I hire them to work at the hotel in various jobs, including personal entertainment when needed. The whole thing seems much more humane. During the three years, a man may negotiate a contract amount, but I have had to hire a watchman, because several couples have even lowered themselves from the balcony. Several of the young women have actually become dear friends, although they usually move back to cities where they can live without moral prejudice.

One of my more illustrious guests, in the motion picture business, is so charmed about what he says is my "modern" ideas of sex, that I should direct some educational films. He says he knows just the gent who could do it. But I think he is teasing me.

On my better days, I imagine this hotel as a kind of "finishing school" for young women who come from desperate or uneducated backgrounds. I look for intelligence, resourcefulness and a kind of spark of life that carries one very far.

I sometimes imagine that your spark carried you far away and you have come to a peaceful and happy place.

Love from the lakeside,

Your Marie

Jackie Henrion

Madame de Pompadour

Madame de Pompadour (née Poisson) divorces her husband to become the royal consort of Louis XV. Her prophecy fulfilled. At the age of nine, a "seer" had predicted little Jeanne-Antoinette would reign over the heart of a king. Her mother and patrons made sure her education and training were pointed in that direction. Francois Boucher, the romantic, allegorical artist, has, by this time painted the intelligent, talented Jeanne-Antoinette Poisson numerous times, never without a corsage of red roses at her left breast. Although she arranges many activities in art, architecture and theatre, she is unable to persuade the King to support writers, until she persuades him to engage Voltaire in April 1745 as court historiographer. She amasses a library of 3525 books, all of which she has leather bound and gilt adorned. By 1750 she understands that the sexual novelty of their relationship is coming to its natural end, but this King Louis is a child-man and knows Jeanne-Antoinette is intelligent and balanced enough to protect him from the worst of court intrigue. She manages his calendar, correspondence and amusements for the next fourteen years until her death. She is not, however, without detractors and the King, watching her cortège from his window, simply states, "Another one, gone."

NAKEDNESS

Dear Niswi,

I must write about nakedness. As I pen these words I am looking at a stripe of blue sky across the horizon, disrobing the day to the heavens. I have noticed a difference amongst the women about how they view their own nudity. Despite their profession, some are very modest about taking off their clothes, preferring to do so behind a screen and emerging only in dim light. It's as if they have taken on the beliefs of their early years and thus the naked skin takes on a "charge" of sexual energy.

I have also noticed that men in particular, who grew to adults never having seen the naked body of a woman without paying for it, find the thought and vision of it so salacious that they can barely control their instincts. Certain women, who have also been raised thus, find that even looking at their naked form in the mirror feels like a terrible evil, which leads to wicked thoughts and deeds. It's as if the leap to a sexual act is an uncontrollable and irrevocable occurrence.

Of course, I discuss this with both of my mentors, Lui and Joseph. Lui takes a rather sanguine view saying that there is nothing inherently wrong or right about nudity. The important thing is to understand that any association can become sexualized. He explains how Chinese history includes the sexualization of a dreadfully deformed foot, only achieved by the most painful mutilation of girls at a very young age. Even the sight of such a foot can drive a man to the height of sexual stimulation. He says the English word for this concentration of psychological energy is 'fetish.' He believes that anything has the capacity to become a fetish. Animals, food, shoes, books, hair, fingernails as well as any part of the human body. But this fetish signals a spirit out of balance. One loses a certain equa-

nimity of being as the obsession appears without awareness.

Joseph also has an interesting viewpoint as a Frenchman. He said that the sexual stimulation is indeed different for every single human and we can experience sexual pleasure from the moment we are born. Further, he suggests that before we are even aware of it, and some are never able to discern the reason, our body creates its own sexual language. But his view is that most people never learn to embrace the feeling of sexual arousal without expectation of the orgasm. Phillips says that it is possible, and even pleasurable, to create and re-create this experience over and over as if riding a wave. He suggests that it enlivens all other experiences to be in such a state. He says that the French have known nakedness in art for thousands of years. It is, for them an exploration, a discussion, a sensory experience without which life becomes flat.

How I miss our own frank talks about all of this. This journal reassures me that your spirit is still with me.

Love, Marie

CASANOVA

I visit the cell in Venice's Doges Palace where Casanova was imprisoned. It is an ample space. The windows have no bars, because it is three stories above the water, and no one in his right mind would jump. Casanova was not in anyone's right mind, and so he persuaded a monk, imprisoned nearby, to help him dig through the walls to escape. On the eve of success, he is transferred to another cell. However, his persuasive charm and enchanting, delicious tales earn him another patron, who helps him climb to the lead roof, then leap to nearby buildings.

I notice a passageway, which descends a narrow stairway. Drifting behind the tour group to explore the staircase, I exit through a mirrored closet door out into a rather grand room on the floor below, much to the surprise of another tour group. Had I worn a feathered bonnet, I would have bowed.

During his time, Venice has approximately 11,000 Courtesans in a population of 100,000. In 1651, British historian James Howell had penned this poem to Venice:

Though, Syren-like on Shore and Sea, Her Face

Enchants all those whom once She doth embrace

Nor is ther any can Her bewty prize

But he who hath beheld her with his Eyes.

In 1789, a group of Venetian women composed a "handbook" for establishing a career as a Courtesan.

One must be intelligent and well educated

One must be introduced, or gain some initial sponsorship

One must be dressed to the latest fashion, with a unique signifying flare

One must have the knowledge of hair dying, braiding and arranging

One must cultivate the skill of gracious communication and the art of listening

One must have a fluid knowledge of poetry and music and amusements

One must be able to convincingly maintain an air of gaiety and joie de vivre

One must be fully comfortable with the language of flirtation, sex and love.

One must be attentive to physical appearance and well-being

One must ask the question, "Other than affairs of the heart, what is your strongest desire in life?"

BETWEEN ECHOES

Thejokingvoices

Which icannottouchbecausetheyaretoonear

Foraminute sufficedatwhattheyare

A gesture I love to beserved

Slidingonoffmylap

heardasifIhadnoEar

Jackie Henrion

VERDI

Giuseppe Verdi and his new wife, Giuseppina Strepponi, attend a performance of the play *La Dame aux Camelias*. It is a miserable, rainy evening. Strepponi, a performing soprano and also a serial paramour, is touched by the moral nobility of the doomed Courtesan. Verdi starts to envision the story with music.

La Traviata

Verdi's opera *La Traviata*, premiers in Venice, based on the libretto developed from Dumas *fils'* story. The Italian censors are concerned about the lax morality. So instead of a contemporary setting, it is set back in time c. 1700. It is too late in the year for camellias, so the soprano who plays Violetta, the doomed heroine, wears red and white roses instead. The performance is booed. Verdi believes the bad reception is due to the well-connected, but matronly, thirty-eight-year-old diva, who was hardly credible playing the nubile young Courtesan.

IMMORAL

*L*a *Traviata* is performed in the United States by the Max Maretzek Italian Opera Company at the recently opened Academy of Music at East 14th St and Irving Place in New York City. The renowned diarist George Templeton Strong notes: "People say the plot's immoral, but I don't see that it's so much worse than many others, not to speak of *Don Giovanni*, which, as put on the stage, is little but rampant lechery."

SURVIVAL

Marie applies to teach school in Hope. Despite her experience and credentials, the position is filled by a local man. Desperate, and after having proven her skill, she has started to work as a dressmaker for the women who work for Joseph Jeannot, owner of the Jeannot Hotel. Marie's intelligence impresses Jeannot and eventually she becomes book-keeper and manager, and ultimately, lover. Both Joseph and the local Chinese Union Boss, Lui Den, mentor her in different ways.

Jackie Henrion

SPENT BLOOM

Placido Domingo stars in the movie of *La Traviata* directed by Franco Zeffirelli. Instead of flowers, Violetta wears red and white gowns. The young Violetta dies of "consumption" in a gown of apricot colored silk. Consumption ~ an historic euphemism for being consumed.

FREUD

E lse Jerusalem, a young philosophy student at the University of Vienna, sees a performance of *La Traviata*. She whispers to her friend, Rachel, "Why does the woman die?" The opera inspires her to research and document the culture of prostitution and brothels in the city and throughout Europe. A frequent attendee of early feminist meetings, she studies John Stuart Mill's essay on *The Subjugation of Women*. She attends lectures given by professor Sigmund Freud, flirts with him, noting in her journal that "he is obsessed with sex, cigars and stories." She becomes close with Emma Eckstein, another lively, intellectual student. Freud and his close friend, surgeon Wilhelm Fliess, take Eckstein as a patient. Eckstein says both men intermittently harass, threaten, abuse, or intimidate her. Jerusalem writes a book titled *Give us the Truth (Gebt uns die Wahrheit)*, which advocates sexual education for young women.

Jackie Henrion

VIPASSANA

I am not able to write about meditation. When I arrive at the center in Onalaska, Washington, I am asked to certify that I will observe Buddhist principles and that I will use no writing implements during my ten days of silence. I can understand the principles, but writing?

I am to learn the art of losing. Even without notes, I recall day seven. I saw my seated self, unraveling like an apple peel, my wedding ring falling to the pebbled beach of Lake Pend Oreille. Tears leaked down my cheeks unchecked.

Only years later, I encounter Elizabeth Bishop's poem "One Art." Years after that, I learn of Chogyam Trungpa Rimpoche's loss of family and homeland, forced to flee on foot, then emigrate to foreign countries to survive. I practice losing farther, losing faster. Ultimately, it leads me to gratitude.

Essay to a Woman

itmaylooklike AJourneytotheSoul

by TenderButtons

                          tomasterthough I Write

andsingmyself

organizingembodiedandtranspersonal

andfromitsdoors

                                 isanemergentself

Hopingtoceasenottilldeath

Jackie Henrion

TIME FRAMED

B each waves were flavored with salt, sauerkraut, Chantilly, and sand. The first letters I learned were 'D' and 'Q' on the large black and orange subways signs from Greenwich Village to Brighton Beach. The approaching thrum of train on track from a black tunnel mouth with a whoosh like a Kerouac poem, as Suzuki Bean once said.

Two little pig-tailed sisters riding the bumps, thrilled with the open-air bridge crossing over the Hudson River and through the open windows of the brick projects. The Beach has more knish and fruit vendors than Bleecker Street. The fishy ocean scent laced with suntan lotion squeezed from brown bottles, labeled with a picture of dog pulling down the panties of a little girl.

Sauerkraut and pickle barrels at the bottom of the train exit steps, I would know even if blindfolded. But blindfolded I wouldn't be able to avoid cracks and black circles on sidewalks. My grandmother's perfume-infused apartment with living-room/beauty parlor. Waves of students flow in and out of the school building across the street.

Can I love a place so much it makes my temples ache?

A skinny, knock-kneed, freckle-faced, buck-toothed girl carries plastic buckets and pails down the overly long concrete steps, under the boardwalk where the fine sand is always grey and cool but leads out to the hot, soft, mounded beach sand. I know these waves like I know myself. Better, even. I was afraid of waves because any deeper than waist high will knock you over. These are not swimming waves, they're jumping waves. They're for arm-flapping like a swamped seagull. Waves that suck the wet sand from under toes and heels leaving stuck lumps under your foot arch. Stand in one place, your balance is ruined, and you feel you could end up in China.

Waves are scary and fun at the same time. Like a new relationship, like agreeing to get married, like trying to get pregnant, like the cyclone ride at Coney Island. Waves like these are perfect for irrigating tunnels and moats in sand castles, then melting the castles back down to wet sand nothings.

Jackie Henrion

Herbals

Among his many responsibilities in the Northwest, Lui Den owns a store which specializes in herbs and "medicinals." These herbs arrive on the Northern Pacific Railroad which brings goods from Seattle, and San Francisco and Portland. Marie is fascinated with his knowledge which he shares, only after they develop a trusting friendship. The two most valued supplies are herbs which act as contraceptives, which supplement the local herbs such as Queen Anne's lace, tansy, slippery elm and skull cap, as well as opium. The other is an herb which combats the sexual diseases of syphilis and gonorrhea. Joseph also depends on Lui's knowledge and recommendations which sometimes contradict the doctor who has settled in Hope. The doctor, originally from Germany at least knows that the "clap" is a bacterial infection. When the ladies complain of such symptoms, he sends them to the doctor for treatment.

After Marie takes over the hotel, things change. The new doctor, an immigrant from England examines the "ladies" every month and teaches them how to examine clients discretely.

Deciphering

So, you are going to let me grow up a little.

I don't have to stay a two-and-a-half-pound lump

lying in a pool of your blood in your bed

in the deserted ward of the hospital?

I would have loved you in that way.

Irrevocable love,

Changing your life forever,

Taking it out of your control

Being needed by another.

You say you resent plants

Which need you to water and feed them.

I would have welcomed that resentment.

I would have gladly been twisted by it.

I would have used it to create my own world.

I would have used the tenacity in our gene pool.

I would have gone out on my own,

Deserted you in time

Jackie Henrion

Like you were deserted.

I am sorry you could not get past the fear

Of imperfection

Dependence until parted by death.

I know now that fear was implanted in you,

Just like I was.

And it won.

COPING

Opium proves to be one of the primary recreations of the Chinese railroad workers, who work ten to twelve-hour days for $1 per day. Despite the Chinese Exclusion Act of 1882, thousands of Chinese were hired to complete the Northern Pacific Railroad. Lui Den organized a regional strike which resulted in a base pay of $1.50; still less than any European immigrants would accept. For decades Den protected, employed and housed hundreds who worked in mining, laundry, farming, food preparation, baggage handlers and numerous other jobs no one else would do. Den also enabled workers to send money back to their families in China. The railroad bosses will not admit publicly that the Chinese workers are more reliable and hard-working, and more skilled with explosives, than any other group.

Jackie Henrion

BURDEN

As I walk towards the Engelhard Court of the Metropolitan Museum with my Mother, she exclaims, "Isn't art transcendent?" Her question bounces off the nearby stone walls in small sharp echoes. After buying salads at the café, we take seats in the light saturated courtyard just behind the golden sculpture of Diana the Huntress. I ask her questions about her adolescence and time as a young mother. Those years are silent in my memory and, from her reaction, she would prefer that they remain so. She says, "I did so many bad things." When I continue to press, she discloses a few of her misadventures. As I listen I realize that in the grand scheme of moral transgressions, these Electra-hued moments are common to many women. Why is she carrying this burden of belief about herself? I start to wonder if 'Art' enabled her to transcend the psychic burden. In a way, that's my sense of my Father as well.

THORNS

I chat with Jenny's Mother, Rosemary, who is also an artist as well as a published writer. She also feels that she did "bad things" in her younger days. Perhaps she disclosed the details with her daughter, because it appears that Jenny agrees with her. The belief adorns both of them.

A New Stance

E lse Jerusalem's book *Der Heilige Scarabäus* revolves around Milada, a child raised in a Viennese brothel. She loves and cares for her mother, despite the latter's vehement hatred towards the man who refuses to marry after sexually taking advantage of her. Milada grows up without any notion that the activities in the brothel are anything but normal. Her first experience of cultural prejudice towards brothels comes as an adult when she is confronted by the complicit interweaving between men, "proper" women, police, laws and moral beliefs. She is astounded and confused. (Unfortunately, the discussion of the complex issue may lie in the 300 pages in the original German edition omitted from the English translation.)

Nonetheless, Milada draws her strength from the transcendent belief in original innocence, the value of education and awareness, and the resultant belief in a woman's power to create a life without regard to conventional moral restrictions. I wonder, how would existence be altered without concepts of good/bad or right/wrong? Could they be replaced by the concept of growth towards light?

I search for a poem on the internet to contemplate conflicting burdens of belief. I find many male poets, but I now choose to focus on the voices of women. Lia Purpura's poem "Belief" at Poetrysociety.org ends with the phrase "...a wobble I think it's time to take seriously as a stance."

GOSSIP

Dear Niswi

I want to share my thoughts on these pages, since I am now left with no other woman in this town willing to discuss their views on subjects which affect us so deeply. Subjects such as masturbation, orgasm, abortion and rape. After all these years, I feel that my perspective has a certain value and authority. I notice so few parents actually speak to their children about these matters, and as a result, it causes much suffering especially for women.

Masturbation: I feel that from the moment we are born, and who knows, perhaps even before, our body becomes aware of the possibilities of pleasurable stimulation. It may happen while sitting in a chair, on a log, a parent's knee, riding a pony, or just by natural exploration of hands over one's body while falling asleep. It seems like such a natural thing to bring such pleasure and yet, the views of it, especially by religions, impart embarrassment, shame, and even sin. Such baggage seems nothing short of crippling to one's humanity. As you and I know, explorations of childhood include sharing such experiences, but inevitably fall to stern condemnation. In the most peculiar perversion, I have seen many who believe that masturbation is worse than the sex act itself, and that doing it before a witness would be the height of mortification. On the other hand, there have been some who develop an obsession to perform it in the presence of others, perhaps even as a result of the shame and prohibition.

It seems to me that loving relationships would be improved greatly if an early step would be to share one's experience, allowing the partner to understand and see how that pleasure develops. In fact, as different modes of stimulation develop, it is particularly helpful for women to understand the possibilities of both external and internal stimulation. It seems to me

Jackie Henrion

from all my years that men have so little opportunity to witness a woman giving herself pleasure, it remains a complete mystery to them and a source of much embarrassment and frustration to learn.

Orgasm: This is truly a little miracle of all human experience. During orgasm we sense the ultimate physical and spiritual connection within the universe. In the time afterward, all things appear relaxed and aligned. I have recently been reading how at that moment, the body's hormones and emotional centers activate a certain grace in demeanor and attitude. An amusing thought once occurred to me, in light of all the wars and wasted human lives in the last 50 years, world leaders should be assembled at a table underneath which they are all brought to a climax at the same time. I believe world peace would be possible in the glow of that moment. I can only imagine that evolution progressed to associate ultimate pleasure with procreation; the ejection spasms in a man matching the suction spasms in a woman.

Abortion: In my lifetime, this issue has been politicized to a horrifying degree. In the business, it is a dismaying reality and only a pragmatic and understanding doctor enables the women to maintain an independent state of mind. In my view, historical feminist philosophy is the only force which advocates for a woman's capacity to choose her future. Here, both religion and conventional medicine conspire to serve the needs and viewpoints of men alone. Luckily herbs and tinctures from both Native and Chinese sources have helped to deal with it realistically. I also understand that there are recent developments in birth control pills, at least this is a step in the right direction. There is no other issue of power and control which lies at the heart of women's independence and freedom.

Rape: I believe that more women are raped within marriage than outside of it. Without doubt, this belief is based on my own personal experience of six years of marital rape before I was fled in desperation. Now with almost half a century of distance, I can see that my first husband suffered from ignorance and a tortured up-bringing which conflated that miraculous orgasmic power as a short-lived cure for low self-esteem and rage. Through much assistance from the wisdom of others, I recognize the resulting scars in my own soul which color my view of men in general. Some men (and women) seem to have very little capacity to heal or grow in this regard. In my view, rape is a violent behavior; an inability to control the emotional energy in behavior and either a lack of consideration or perversity about the effect of fear, pain or physical harm. The sexual urge should never be weaponized. It is never the victim's fault.

Je t'embrace, Marie

Jackie Henrion

Beliefs Are Not What We Think

Beliefs are formed by a network of neural synapses which fire together based on experience. "Cells that fire together, wire together" is derived from psychologist Ernest Hebb's law: "Let us assume that the persistence or repetition of a reverberatory action (or "trace") tends to induce lasting cellular changes that add to its stability.[...] When an axon of cell A is near enough to excite a cell B and repeatedly or persistently takes part in firing it, some growth process or metabolic change takes place in one or both cells such that A's efficiency, as one of the cells firing B, is increased.

Hebb's theories have influenced the latest research in neuropsychology. Contrary to previous traditional theories of childhood psychology, "beliefs" are formed as soon as neurons begin to fire, even in the womb. The formation is strengthened by strong emotional associations such as pain, shame, and grief. In new mindfulness/happiness philosophies, this perspective helps people understand how the formation of their beliefs are therefore "innocent" and entirely malleable. In other words, our capacity to change is more like water than 'old dogs.'

A Cutting

Else Jerusalem is cut from her creative stem by a love affair with a military nobleman who transports her to his homeland in Venezuela. She has converted from Judaism to Catholicism, which is not uncommon, and makes no difference to her, until she arrives in Buenos Aires. There she experiences the full constraint of a Catholic patriarchal culture. Not even her Salons, attended by brilliant minds such as Albert Einstein, can restore her spirits for long.

In Front

Iwantedtobe

Beyondthisplaceofwrathandtears

asifthemiraclewere

Bornhere

AFairerhousethanprose

lastornext

andagaintothisonetelling

acrosstheyard

Someofusstoodaround

last

andalsocertainlyalsoaprison

VALUES OBSERVED
BY MARIE

Joseph Jeannot Values	Lui Den Values
Humor	Peace of mind
Sensuality	Respect
Beauty	Poetry
Appreciation of women	Contemplation
Sexuality	Nature's beauty
Natural imperfection	Wisdom
Hospitality	Self-sacrifice for community
Graciousness	Hard work
Opportunity	Focus of attention
Philosophy	Respect of Ancestors
Intellect	Humility

Sexual Pleasure vs. Sex Acting

An Ellipsis

Organic
personal
reassuring
antidotal
transcendent
natural
reliable
simple
pure
direct
accessible

Curious
tit for tat
confused
faked
desired
empowering
peopled
commodified
resisted
colonized
irrelevant

sweet
integrated

TRANSLATION

Dear Niswi:

I will try to narrate what Joseph said today. I continue to take on more responsibility at the hotel, but I have expressed my discomfort on numerous occasions. As you and I know, the views of men and women differ greatly, although you always seemed to grasp both sides, as well as a combined sense. It was good, after all, that your mother waited until you were older to give you the name Three Spirit. As Joseph is the owner, I defer to him in most things, but I will have to consider his statements. Here is the best I can remember:

"What shall we say of this business: necessary, is it not? To what do we respond? To life itself. What we call 'la petite mort,' is it not the final connection with nature, the transcendent? We resist the rules, flout the laws, yet we must obey the one true aspect of our existence. All else is petty, without importance.

Sex work. Why must we name it so? Let us consider that nature has given us this energy to move forward, to re-create, to connect in a fashion like no other. Why must we make it dirty? Why not divine? Worthy of worship? That we debase it, use the language of violence, of cruelty, of danger, a view which serves only to make the human as animal.

Do I sound crazy? Do I fool myself to think that the women may not find pleasure simply due to the money for a transaction? They may choose. They have a certain power ... you know, not possible from the other ways, if we do not look closely, we do not use the right words, which reveal our intentions. For what else do we search?

For a woman has the reckless inner need as well, and after all, energy

Jackie Henrion

will make itself known - a kind of discovery - irresistible, that pulls us into expression. In this fashion, I am for women as much as they are for me."

Sometimes he speaks in riddles, I will have to consider his words to see if I agree.

Yours always, Marie

EXPLOITATION

Webster's Third New International Dictionary

A. Utilization or working of a natural resource: a wasteful or destructive use of a natural resource.

B. An unjust or improper use of another person for one's one profit or advantage; utilization of the labor power of another person without giving a just or equivalent return.

C. Coaction between organisms in which one is benefitted at the expense of the other - used especially of relationships in which the effect is less extreme than parasitism or predation.

Jackie Henrion

Discovering

thehourbadlyspent

mysoul

belongingtome

Ilfautbienquelecorpsexulte [the body must rejoice]

asgoodbelongstoyou

    foraminutealone

        tendre

      andstumbling

TOUCHSTONE

Dear Niswi

You continue to be my touchstone. I don't know how I could have found my way over the last ten years without thinking of your spirit always with me. Most of the women in the town shun me, so the only solace has been one other person; White Bear Woman, a strange name for a woman who has very dark skin, who lives with a man named Carl Ninneman, related to Clinton's family. They stop by our store then pack the goods by horse up to a little cabin way up in the mountain above East Hope. He has invented the most interesting ways to get water and even power from the stream which runs nearby. Sometimes we laugh about him peaking in at the window of the school to watch the teachers who do only a fair job with the twenty or so students from the town. The young ones work at the sawmills mostly though, so it is difficult to learn anything more than the basic skills in writing, reading and math. All my efforts to assist there are in vain, especially now that the town's women consider me tainted by my association with the hotel.

I have also met a native woman named Christine who writes under the name of Mourning Dove. Her spirit reminds me of you. She also believes in that special power you described. She calls it "Shumix." She has never married but she attends the enormous celebration held at the nearby Clark Fork Delta in September. So many different people come all the way from the Pacific Coast to the plains in Montana and the Dakotas. They play many games, pick berries, trade goods and enjoy themselves immensely. I told her about us — she seems to understand very well. But of course, you know that our special love can never be replaced in my heart.

Yours always,   Marie

Jackie Henrion

Uttanasana
Intense Forward Bending Pose

One of my yoga teachers at Seattle's Eight Limbs Studio once suggested that this pose could be a meditation on humility. For many years I was not humble. Perhaps because I don't like the word. All show of humility seems false. Obsequious. On the other hand, it reverberates with attempts to control others. A finger waving back and forth. However, I am still under the illusion of control, at least over myself. Illusion, Allusion, Delusion.

After five years I was able to place my hands on the floor. The most powerful muscles in my body still striving. Faith: one day my muscles will trust me enough to allow my head to rest on my knees. As I breath into this pose my stomach draws in towards my back, and if I have eaten something off, I can feel the soreness in my intestines. Shifting my weight from my heels, through feet to hands, the thought of sharing the weight occurs to my limbs. Bearing weight, sharing weight. Isn't that why we reach for others?

SANDPOINT SENTINEL

*C*linton Root was found dead in his bed at the Jeannot Hotel. Initially it appeared that he died of natural causes or heart attack, but when he was lifted from the bed into a coffin, a lead plug dropped from his ear. One witness commented on the bizarre circumstance, "It was as if hot molten lead had been poured into his ear." He is survived by an aunt, uncle, two nephews, one niece, and his beloved wife, Marie Root of Hope, Idaho.

His death remains an unsolved mystery.

NEW DEAL

Marie acquires the Jeannot Hotel. Jeannot lost it in a gambling bet. She redeems the debt with her savings from the last 12 years.

She changes the culture. She recruits from Spokane, Seattle and even San Francisco with a specific set of skills and attitudes, frequently redeeming women from desperate living conditions. She explains the term 'volition.' The women learn and work at sewing, cooking, and housecleaning for a contracted term. The contracts may be bought out if the circumstances can be negotiated. She fills the grounds with the most fragrant antique rose bushes, each of which she roots with cuttings collected or received as gifts. She writes in her journal that the roses are seductive, scented and thorny. She continues to operate the Hotel until 1962 with a full range of hospitality services. She occasionally reduces the price to men who are able to "respect and please the ladies in return."

She changes the name to the Hotel Hope.

MR. WASSAN SINGH

Dear Niswi,

It has been a very peculiar day. It started in the late morning as the train stopped and a small group of passengers disembarked. The Chinese workers went to collect the baggage and the carriage was sent down the hill for our lodgers. Mr. Wassan had telegraphed his intent to stay with us for five days. When he arrived, the grace of his posture and movements was noticeable, along with a complete patience with the baggage handling and settling in. His dark black hair was smoothed back from a high forehead and his skin is the color of dark honey, like yours. He seemed almost regal, with an accent that was British and musical. When I mentioned that the bar opened at 2 in the afternoon and we offered other hospitality services, he just smiled slightly and shook his head saying, "No need, thank you." That kind of response usually makes me a little nervous, since prohibition laws went into effect seven years ago. But he was like a bear, simply shaking off the rain from his fur. My guess would be that he was not quite six feet tall and when he hefted one of his valises up the stairs he did not strain in the least.

He stayed in his room until dinner time. That was strange enough, since most visitors are eager to explore the lake or forest, but when Lilly went in to bring in linens and turn down the bed, he was in the midst of stretching in the most bizarre poses. She almost fled from the room in fright, but I told her I would get to the bottom of it at dinner.

As I hosted the dinner guests, the impression of strangeness deepened. When I offered wine, or any of our spirits, he declined and, "Simply water." Water! I had to send one of the girls out to the fresh water fountain, recently installed on the road, since all of our spigots supply cleaning and toilet

Jackie Henrion

water. Nor was that all. When I described the dinner fare, he asked if it would be possible to have a plate of vegetables; any and all the vegetables we had available, since he ate no meat. Thank goodness the Chinese gardeners grow an array of greens! The cook just grinned and bobbed his head, coming up with a selection of spinach with garlic, a combination of Chinese greens, carrots, and rice with green onions, soy sauce and eggs. Mr. Wassan seemed delighted.

After dinner, I was able to sit with Mr. Wassan. He was a gracious guest and shared quite a remarkable story, after telling me that his full name was Wassan Singh. He said,

"I immigrated from Delhi, India at a young age, along with my father. I worked at many lumber mills in the Pacific Northwest, and comradeship was good, but the pay was bad and so was the health of most of the workers. I could see that attempts at labor organization faced complex problems. The health of my co-workers was at risk, not only because of the conditions in the mills, but because they didn't have any knowledge about their body's flexibility, resilience, mental health and even the food they ate. I was brought up in a household which practiced the ancient Indian lifestyle of Yoga philosophy."

At that point he stopped talking, apparently gauging my reaction. I had never heard of the concept, and he seemed earnest enough, so I said, "I am curious to hear more about this."

He was quiet for a moment and perhaps even closed his eyes. I noticed how thick his lashes were and that the shape of his brow was perfectly curved. Then he began "Yoga is a deep and multi-layered philosophy with a lineage stretching many thousands of years, but there are some very simple practices which improve one's life right away. The fundamental principle is that we do better if we become more aware of how our body works. He says it is the vehicle for doing much good, even though our time in this body is only temporary. With care and attention to how we move, how we eat, how we speak, we learn that the mind may help us transcend our suffering."

After he said that, I remembered a similar statement Lui had made about his Buddhist beliefs. I thought of all the people who come to the hotel looking for ways to ease the pain of their daily life, by the solace of sex, by liquor or drugs. By the next morning, they return to their pain. Over and over they repeat, without ever seeming to find a real cure. So, I said as much.

He said, "How perceptive you are. There are indeed shared beliefs between the great philosophies and those of Asia are the oldest. Even the ancient Greek philosopher, Pyrrhus, learned from our Indian sages while he accompanied Alexander the Great on his campaigns."

I realized I was talking to a young man whose knowledge was far beyond his years. But I have to break off this letter to get the ladies set up for their night duties. I will continue soon.

You remain in my thoughts,

Marie

Jackie Henrion

PRACTICE

Dear Niswi

I was not able to get back to my journal for a number of days, since Mr. Wassan, as he prefers to be called, is now conducting a little class for myself and the ladies in this philosophy called Yoga. He began by intoning some thoughts that we are to keep in our heads at the start of each session, which I will try record with as much accuracy as possible:

"I invite you to become aware of your breathing. How the exhale, if continued for a bit longer through slightly compressed lips, then pulls air automatically into the body naturally, without thought. You may notice that during some of the positions, your breath will come more quickly. That is a sign that your body feels it needs more air based on old beliefs that are fearful of the unfamiliar. It will stabilize as you hold the pose, until your body becomes more accustomed to it and can slow down to its natural rhythm.

Do not think of this practice as exercise. These poses, developed over thousands of years are meant to open a dialog between your mind and your body. As you hold the pose, called "Asana," do not think of what you need to achieve, but rather, what your body will allow. This is not about striving to achieve perfection, as each of us will have a different capacity. It is about permitting the leverage of the pose to affect your muscles, ligaments, other organs and systems to expand without anxiety."

Some of the poses are very simple, some are comically difficult and more than one of us has ended up on the floor, flushed from exertion. He constantly reminds us to be compassionate with ourselves and to avoid exertion, which is philosophically seen as 'striving towards' or 'fearful against.' I

Rerooted

must say, that after only four days, my body feels more limber and fit than I have in years. The ladies all gather round after dinner, asking him questions and to speak more about the philosophy. I can hardly get them to flirt with the other patrons at all.

He is certainly not an expensive boarder; he drinks no alcohol, does not take advantage of the feminine services, and eats only fruits, vegetables and eggs. He has also been filling our heads with notions about the food we eat and how it is either medicine or poison. He says that as we proceed with the 'Asana,' we will become more aware of how our body feels after each meal and choose accordingly.

I invited him to stay longer, but he declined, saying that he will be traveling to Oklahoma City, where he has a number of influential friends. He hopes to bring his yoga philosophy to many more people. I asked him to correspond so that I may hear more about his progress.

Sending my thoughts and love,

Marie

Telegram

To: Lui Den, Twin Woo Company, Hope, Idaho

From: M. Root, San Francisco

Dear Lui,

I have interviewed a number of women (stop) There is a young Chinese girl here who goes by the name of May (stop) Works almost as a slave in one of the houses (stop) She barely speaks English, but has a delicacy and intelligence much above her duties (stop) Will you help me with her? (stop)

To M. Root, San Francisco

From: L Den, Twin Woo Company, Hope, Idaho

Yes (stop)

The Name Of A Rose

Dear Niswi

Lui asks me questions which provoke my thinking. It began as we sat on the veranda looking out over the lake reflecting the mountains. The water was as calm as the moments of silence between his questions. After I offered him a cut blossom from the vase he had given to me as a gift, he asked for the name of the flower.

It pleased me to tell him the name was "Peace," a rose first presented on the day Berlin fell to the allies in World War II. Developed by M. Meilland, it was sent to the English commander responsible for the strategy which ended the war, along with a note "We hope the 'Peace' rose will influence men's thoughts..." I said it was a fitting sentiment and history for cultivation at the Hotel.

He closed his eyes to inhale the strong, spicy fragrance. He asked if it ever occurred to me that the thorns on the stem signaled the rose's awareness that its physical beauty and scent would be irresistible otherwise. This led to an engaging discussion of awareness, intelligence, and even survival.

He then asked how I knew of roses. I related our childhood together when your Grandmother showed us her collection of herbs including ogin-üg (rose hips) and how we delighted in finding the wild roses the very next spring.

After a long silence he then asked why I choose to cultivate these roses. When I responded with all the formal reasons about growing temperatures and conditions, he slowly shook his head, saying "Tell me something deeper about these particular flowers. Are not camellias, chrysanthemums or peonies equally as beautiful?"

Jackie Henrion

His question shocked me a bit, so I narrated the rose's history. I explained my attraction to the classic shape of buds and blossoms and the yellow/honey/red tinged hues of my "Peace" Tea Rose.

But he also wondered about other associations and metaphors. I finally felt that I might trust him enough to disclose a poem by William Butler Yeats, whose meaning filled my heart when I first heard it. It was called "The Lover Tells of The Rose In His Heart:"

All things uncomely and broken, all things worn out and old,

The cry of a child by the roadway, the creak of a lumbering cart,

The heavy steps of the ploughman, splashing the wintry mould,

Are wronging your image that blossoms a rose in the deeps of my heart.

The wrong of unshapely things is a wrong too great to be told;

I hunger to build them anew and sit on a green knoll apart,

With the earth and the sky and the water, re-made, like a casket of gold

For my dreams of your image that blossoms a rose in the deeps of my heart.

After I recited the poem, he nodded his head, saying, "The meanings we hold close are made of many sources of light. Illumination comes by flashes or rays which coalesce to form a whole picture. Seeing the whole picture is as rare and passionate as Yeats' love for Maud Gonne Have you heard of her?" His knowledge of Gonne shocked me, as I have followed every detail of her struggles, as if they were my own. Perhaps, in many ways, they are. The way he looked out over the lake as he asked it, I felt he wasn't expecting me to answer right away.

I don't know why his words bring me such calm. Like a song remembered. In the glow of it, even losing you seems less painful, more poignant.

With love,

Marie

Rerooted

Paraphrase

A woman student in a university class on mythology, conducted by Joseph Campbell, asks "You speak so often of a man's journey, but what about a woman's journey?" He replies, "Women don't go on journeys, they are the journey's purpose. They are, when they come to know, the sacred chalice which men seek."

Jackie Henrion

OLGA COLBRON

The Macaulay Company Inc. publishes an English translation of *Der Heilige Skarabäus* by Austrian, Else Jerusalem. The translator is listed as R.I. Marchant, a pseudonym of Olga Colbron. Colbron, is an author and translator of numerous German books for Macaulay, including mysteries and children's books. After she sees the movie *The Red Kimona* [sic], she believes the English publication of *Der Heilige Skarabäus* is likely to be more accepted as serious literature. However, Colbron cuts 300 pages from its original 600, and changes the title to *The Red House.*

A Dream

I wake from a dream. I am breathing underwater in close prox-
imity to a platypus and a quince. This is the second occurrence
of this dream, so I take notes, even though still foggy at nearly 5
am. I have no direct experience with either, other than the memory
of childhood delight when I first learned of this furry, duck-billed,
beaver-like experiment of nature. A marsupial, which exists only
in Australia, is one of the most ancient mammals on the planet. It
reminds me of the book *The Five Children and It* by Edith Nesbit.
I don't remember the plot, only the sense that a furry potbellied
talking monkey asked many questions and recounted puzzles of
wisdom to the children. I take it from my mind that this platypus
has that same quality. As we float in the water I feel intermittent
pulses from the movement of the animal's tail. The tail is telling a
tale, a story of energy encoded and sensed through the water by my
skin.

But what of the quince? I believe its source is also foreign.
Then I remember my only direct experience was finding a quince
tree nearby in Hope at an unoccupied house with a for sale sign.
I took a few of the hard, yellow fruits home and when I found its
identity as an ingredient in quince jelly and pie I bit into it. My reaction to the bitter flavor, like a lemon crossed with an apple, was
not pleasant. But as I delve into its history I find the following:

It is a member of the genus Cydonia of the rose family: Rosaceae

Its origins are Turkey, Afghanistan, Greece and China

The Portuguese word 'marmelo' is the origin for the word marmalade

It can be boiled and fermented to make a fragrant liquor and digestive

It is propagated through cuttings, not from seed. Like a rose.

That's What

Food

rivers

Poem

by

theMind

Emergent

selforganizingembodiedandtranspersonal

Interview with Emma

Q: Did you know Marie Root?

A: Yes, I met her a number of times. She was well known before the highway came through. Before that there was only the rail, trails and boats which came to the town. She ruled the roost here. But mostly I knew her by reputation.

Q: What kind of reputation did she have?

A: She was all hoity-toity with her business, but she got involved with all the nasty business of prostitution, drugs and drinking, mostly all illegal, but since she had all the men in town wrapped around her little finger, nothing happened to her.

Q: What do you mean about all the men?

A: Well, she had an affair with the owner of the hotel. And that was before her husband Clinton died. That is, if they were even married. There was a rumor that they didn't actually get hitched until years after they got here, when they travelled to Grange Idaho to do it. But then she had the affair with the hotel owner and Clinton ended up dead real quick-like. Then there were rumors that the Justice of the Peace (a nice Irish guy who recited poetry) was also under her spell and the Doc too. She was also pretty thick with that Chinese guy.

Q: Did you actually see any prostitutes?

A: Well, it's not like they hung around town much. But after she took over the hotel from Jeannot, I remember hearing that a miner, who had come into town by boat, roughed up one of "her girls" pretty good. She sent word out and the men dragged the guy, dead drunk, out of the hotel, put him back on his boat and towed him to the center of the lake where they left him without any paddles. But that could have just been rumor.

Q: Are there any other stories about her?

A: Oh, I remember one that happened after the road was paved in front of the hotel. She hated the cars coming through and she especially hated when they parked in front of the hotel and blocked the view of the lake. So, when they ignored her signs, she threw the chamber pots off the balcony on to the cars. By the time the rumor was going around the story was changed to a potful of spaghetti, but we all knew what that meant.

Q: What other things did you experience first-hand?

A: Well, there is one that I feel terrible about...

Q: Such as...??

A: I'd been friends with May, the wife of the Chinese man, Twin Woo [*sic*]. She had a passel of cute kids and sometimes I used to help her care for them. The kids used to bring me fruits and vegetables from the garden and even berries from the hillsides, they were all so sweet and respectful. But one day, May came to the house and begged me to hide her. She said her husband was away in Spokane and Marie was in Seattle, so neither of them could protect her.

She had gone to the doctor for an exam, after which he told

Jackie Henrion

her he had to operate on her. It was clear she didn't want any operation and she was frantic. I calmed her down a bit, thinking that she was exaggerating. But an hour later, there were four men at the door, almost knocking it down. They pulled her out of the house, while she was wailing, and I couldn't do anything about it. I never saw her again.

Q: What happened to her?

A: I heard that they did an operation. No one said anything to Twin Woo. But a week later, May hanged herself.

Q: Do you have any idea why?

A: I don't know for sure, but I heard some men talking later on and one said, "Hell, she already had four of them..." A couple of months later, Twin Woo packed up the family and left town. I believe he moved to Spokane.

KAIROS

Dear Lui,

I am writing you to tell you that I finally agree with your notion that it is time to retire. Jim at Northern Pacific came by to say that the train will no longer stop in the town since there are so few passengers and very little freight. Jim sends his regards. I guess they don't think our groceries and supplies are important. Ah, what a difference from the old days when you were the primary source of income and trade here in Hope. The new owners have painted your buildings mint green, obviously without any notion of the beautiful celadon color you had used to honor your ancestors. Now as a bar and rooming house they fairly crawl with drunks and drug-addled troublemakers. Thank goodness they are too lazy to walk the twelve hundred feet to the hotel. But I remember every step of that walk to you and your family's nurturing embrace.

Since the highway was completed last year barely anyone uses the old road in front of the Hotel. The locals still make me angry, though, by parking right in front, and I only regret that we no longer have chamber pots to empty off the balcony to discourage them. Harry hasn't visited with his Hollywood friends since he married that actress Kathryn a number of years ago.

Occasionally I see Emma, but she can barely look at me for the guilt of what she didn't do to protect May all those years ago. That sinister Dr. MacGruder battled with stomach cancer for a very long time before he passed away. Contrary to all your advice about equanimity, I was glad to see him suffer. I still visit May's grave often to adorn it with my best and most beloved roses. I talk to her and share my favorite memories and worries about the future. She was so young, but losing that child left her in such despair ... Somehow when I speak to her I feel her peaceful, joyful energy and it restores me. I send my love to your four other children and all your grandchildren who must be growing up fast.

You may have heard by now that our efforts to save the Chinese cemetery at least preserved some of the ground where all those men rest. The wall they built to secure the grounds rises up dramatically from the road and now, in the fall, the trailing vines turn a bright lantern red. I wonder, did you plan it that way? Without you, there is no one to maintain the place and it shows nothing but neglect. Once I retire, even my small efforts will disappear.

I remember you mentioned that you have a good lawyer in Spokane. If you would give me his name, I would like to speak to someone about setting up my estate and arranging for the sale of the hotel. It may need a little upgrade, but of course, the bones are still beautiful and Joseph's decision to build with concrete means that it may be the last structure standing in this wasting town.

I look forward to speaking with you and seeing you soon, as my thoughts are to move to an apartment in Spokane. You are, after all, the closest I have to family that has any mutual regard.

With warmest sentiment, your friend,

Marie

Encore

Memoryanddesirestirring

              fromacertainbalcony

touchingskillfully

        Mondoux [my sweetheart] oflostdoorkeys

        TogatherParadise

andwhereitwasyoumeant

anditdoesmoretothat

        somewhereihavenevertravelled

Jackie Henrion

BONSAI

I am recounting the idea for my historical novel about Marie Root to Richard. Only one of Marie's close friends witnessed her peaceful death in 1968, in her apartment in Spokane. La Dame En Rose. I tell him that Marie, like a bonsai tree, rooted, evolved, and flourished despite the meager soil of North Idaho cultural mores.

I have seen such a tree on the tip of the Hope peninsula.

He laughs.

At This Age

anicelymappedface

form'dfromthissoil

Some licked corn, some fully which flicked

licked fully flicked some

corn fully some scorn

Moijesaistoustessortilèges [I know your tantrums]

Tuavaisperdu [You have lost]

howdidthishappen?

c'estl'amourfol [it's crazy love]

Jackie Henrion

EULOGY

BY MASON DEN

This afternoon, I was honored to witness the passing of a dear friend, Marie Root. When I first arrived by her bedside, I asked if she wanted me to call an ambulance to transport her to the hospital. She said no, that she would prefer to choose her place, as she did for most of her life. Her experiences of hospitals were filled with the sadness of ill-health and death. Instead she wanted to focus on gratitude provided by each moment of her life.

She said, "The beginning and end were difficult, but the bloom was magnificent!"

I will always speak of Marie in the present, for she belongs to that state of being more than anyone I have known. To mention details of her life would be like trying to describe a portrait by the shape of the artist's pencil points.

As I waited by her bedside, she spoke with eyes closed, saying simply, "I am ready." At the moment of transition, I was surprised to observe the muscles of her face relax, leaving only the suggestion of a smile.

Splinter

(After Emily Dickinson "The Brain Within Its Groove")

Marie's role as hostess gave her opportunity to meet a number of influential and powerful men from the Spokane area only ninety miles away. Such men were the developers of an area originally called Montrose, an overlooking hill just south of the city. In 1904 the owner of the land negotiated a donation to the city as a park in exchange for water, power and transportation, which would enable the development of numerous houses surrounding the park. The new name for the park was "Manito," an alternate spelling of Manitou, the Native American word for spirit.

The name held significant resonance for Marie, whose journal letters to Niswi Manitou were a daily ritual. This park, which she visited often, was crowned with a hill where wild roses grew in abundance. The original wild roses were actually the variety of 'Sweetbriar' or Shakespeare's 'Eglantine Rose'. Ultimately this site was chosen to be a formal rose garden.

Marie was inspired to study and cultivate the genus, specializing in the most fragrant heritage roses. Many of these were named for famous women and mistresses such as: Empress Josephine (1824), Duchessse de Angoulême (Marie-Antoinette's daughter 1821), and Louise Odier (1851). Her fragrant roses adorned almost every room in the Hotel Hope and likely some were sent along to the Venetian Styled Davenport Hotel.

Against The Grain of Closure

(After Anne Waldman Outrider)

The word rose comes from the feminine Latin word *rosa*. *Sub rosa* is a Latin term meaning "Under the rose." Information shared while standing under the rose was understood as secret. The symbol of the rose appears in government and administrative private chambers and meeting halls. However, I recall a thought by Anne Waldman, "We have to find a way to receive alternative information." Amidst the noise there is a place of silence. I sense that women are designed to understand silence.

In 1947 the Spokane Rose Society was founded based on the initial plantings on Rose Hill in Manito Park. In 1968, the year of Marie's death, the garden doubled its population of heritage species, funded also with a large donation from an anonymous source.

The term *sub rosa* comes to mind as I read through the list of the forty-eight original women members in the charter of the Spokane Rose Society. Marie's name does not appear.

I recall the voice of Milada in Else Jerusalem's *The Red House* as she envisions a place of presence:

...let me lie out in the woods one whole day, where I shall see nothing but the trees, the sky...as if the earth had something to tell me."

Although we say roses have thorns, they are more properly called "prickles;" sickle shaped growths of the stem used for the purpose of securing the branches as they grow outward and upward. In a sense, the rose scrambles towards the light with searing intent.

To Root a Rose

Cut a new growth stem at a forty-five-degree angle to avoid systemic damage

Remove the almost spent blossom to preserve energy

Prune all but three top leaves to concentrate the absorption of light

Split bottom end just below the 'bud' to encourage new root growth

Dip the stem into a small amount of growth enhancer

Place into soil after creating a finger deep depression, fill and pack snugly

Soil should be rich and moist to circulate nutrients

Moisture should be well drained to permit waste disposal and discourage rot

Place in indirect sun so as not to overheat

Protect with a glass jar to support early growth

Systemic

I am walking through the still dormant bushes in the Rose Hill Garden at Manito Park. The chilly air is flavored with moist loamy earth so eager to feed it inspires my lungs to draw in deeply. Caretakers are raking the straw and mulch from around the clipped stalks. I ask about the garden's history, the founders, the origins of the root stocks. One man tells me of the land developers and speculators who made a fortune by selling lots and houses around the park but says nothing of the history of the roses.

The head gardener, says that they no longer accept donations of roses apparently thinking that I might want to donate. He says most of the modern plantings of 'teas' and hybrids come in nine-packs from commercial sources. He recalls that the last donation was in the late sixties.

I ask him if he remembers the type of rose. He says, "I believe it was Rosa Mundi" Rose of the World. First introduced in 1581. One of the most fragrant of the heirlooms, it was named after Rosamond Clifford, beloved mistress of King Henry II of England in 1174.

When the weather warms I will return to the garden to witness, like Milada, "Until a thousand little tiny shoots spring up." I nod my head to the pattern — another fold in the procession.

Afterward

From *Epic of Ishtar and Gilgamesh*

Earliest known writing tablets ca. 3700 b.c.

Translated by Hamilton 1901

"... Oh, could we hear those whispering roses sweet,

Three beauties bending till their petals meet,

And blushing, mingling their fragrance there

In language yet unknown to mortal ear..."

Jackie Henrion

ANTECEDENTS

"Use this word in a sentence" was a primary school assignment I dreaded. My mother dredged up notebooks filled with my desultory attempts: "I don't have a **dog**...My brother ate **breakfast**... We have many **stores** on our street...I **climb** up to my 'bunc' bed..." And so it went for the first half of my life and career: Writing was merely a tool to describe a literal life. My words were stuck at the surface. Sentences were lackluster, even as my vocabulary expanded. Moreover, I was a prodigious reader, giving lie to the maxim, because reading doesn't make you a good writer any more than watching movies makes you a good director.

Then everything changed. I retired early from work and was able to shift my focus to songwriting and ultimately poetry. Studying Emily Dickinson's poem "I dwell in possibility", I was jolted by an insight: We may live on the surface, but we dwell at depths and heights only bounded by our imagination. In other words, there are no boundaries except those created in our mind by our own limited experience. I realized I had missed that crucially important yet subtle lesson. I could have written sentences like:

Eating **breakfast,** I long for a fireplace.

My Dad **stores** his anger, but I blow mine into balloons.

I am afraid to **climb** because you never fall up.

By the time I applied to Naropa's MFA program in Creative Writing, I also wanted to "dwell in possibility." The school's unique pedagogy provided me with perspectives to do so. Early in the program, I suggested the trope that everything could be related to everything else. Imaginative skill is developed by taking random, disparate words and creating — or inviting — a connection. I preserve it as an important belief underlying my work.

Thanks to Gabrielle Civil's gentle but firm suggestion to witness difference, I used a multi-cultural approach to memoir, I also saw how the cacophony of my childhood in Greenwich Village could co-exist with the silence found in forests of north Idaho, where I now live. This paradox of place and space is described articulately by Gloria Anzaldúa's concept "Nepantla," as she expands upon Carl Jung, by saying:

> if you hold opposites long enough without taking sides, a new identity emerges...from the in-between place of Nepantla, you see through the fiction of the monoculture...

I have taken the title of Anzaldúa's essay as a call to action for my writing, which is:

Let us shift...conocimiento...inner work, public acts

Shifting from the personal, private voice of Dickinson, became possible through the community at Naropa. During a series of experiments in co-creation, Kazim Ali asked us to read philosopher Paul Virilio's *Administration of Fear,* which theorizes that the speed of information instills fear. However, that same speed also enables us to collaborate with a multitude of perspectives, a belief I prefer. As an example, Ali suggested *Sappho's Gymnasium*: A collaboration between Olga Broumas and T Begley, who improvised phrases based on Sappho's poetry, then collaborated from afar. I allude to that speed in my work as I shift between voices, across history and space. In this way, a project I had originally envisioned as a second person omniscient narrative about Marie Root expanded to a multigenre community of women's voices.

Anzaldúa explained 'conocimiento.' as knowledge informed by conscious awareness. This awareness recognizes that the unspoken is as potent as the spoken. Especially with regard to the communication between women. In search of a theoretical distinction, I examined the 1986 research text, *Women's Ways of Knowing* by Belenky, Clinchy, Goldberger and Tarule, and a subsequent 2002 anthology of essays about a qualitative method of acquiring knowledge, *Up Close and Personal: The Teaching and Learning of Narrative Research.* In the latter text, Margot Ely writes, "I was working to build a collage a person could walk into, something palpable. Something consonant with qualitative presentation forms that send messages above and beyond their words." The thesis of both books posits knowledge acquisition as "constructed:," and an awareness that beliefs contribute to our perception of reality.

A portion of my conceptual construction *Rerooted,* is poetry created from unparsed phrases taken from poems "I hold in my heart" as Sei Shonagon called forth in *The Pillow Book.* These poems and other books are listed in the Appendix. From the text of these works, I use a chance generator application called Word*Palette*. The application enables a poetic method, whose ancestry is found in Surrealist, Dada, Beat, and Language schools. Compelling phrases are compressed for the application, a compression I chose to retain. In this way the reader is invited to focus on decoding, which is a metaphor for my experience with radio encoding and transmission. Much as Shonagon quotes and updates historical poetry, the re-use is both an homage and a new resonance, an echo.

Anzaldúa defined herself as a lesbian queer mestiza activist. By embracing and transcending these identifications, her work appeared to shift from her 1981 anthology, *This Bridge Called My Back: Writings by Radical Women of Color*, which emphasized the realities of marginalized identities ~ to the 2002 anthology, *This*

Bridge We Call Home: Radical Visions for Transformation. In the latter, her forty-page essay describes the "inner work" necessary to transform. The Naropa 2017 Summer Writing Program provided me with such opportunities. For example, the marathon schedule required compassion for myself and others, on a deeper level than I had experienced before. New and challenging intellectual material became more accessible through meditation, movement and music. I felt at once both energized and peaceful.

Sara Veglahn's guidance during a survey of "Contemporary Trends" inspired another shift. One of her assigned texts was John D'Agata's anthology *The Next American Essay*. D'Agata, editor of the journal *Seneca Review*, suggests the sub-genre "Lyric Essay" as a catch-basin for work which neither conforms to previous classification, nor pledges allegiance to fiction or fact:

> The lyric essay...takes the subjectivity of the personal essay and the objectivity of the public essay and conflates them into a literary form that relies on both art and fact, on imagination and observation, rumination and argumentation, human faith and human perception.

However, it is worth noting that a number of women writers, including Rebecca Solnit, Lia Purpura and Mary Ruefle disclaim this "sub-genre." Their reluctance suggests that classification itself becomes a belief system, by which we herd creativity into marketing stockades. The so-called 'hybrid' forms of Eleni Sikelianos, Susan Howe, and Anne Carson also challenge convention. As they demonstrate, even without genre differentiation, the essay and hybrid forms, both have the capacity to shift and stretch organically, embracing ambiguity. My creative choice is to purposefully engage that ambiguity, in both poetic theory and conceptual essay.

Most of my life has been informed by the perspective and

Jackie Henrion

language of men. But Naropa led me to an appreciation of encoded 'silence' found in women's essays such as Sei Shonagon's command of "time" in *The Pillow Book*. A unique perspective was also evident in Susan Griffin's "Red Shoes," Mary Reufle's "Monument," and Theresa Hak Kyung Cha's "Erato." In fact, all thirteen essays written by women in D'Agata's anthology are potent examples of a unique relationship to time, space and ideation. I went on to examine gender literary theory by Judith Butler and Jane Donawerth's *Rhetorical Theory by Women before 1900*. Further readings included *Doing Time* by Rita Felski and Julia Kristeva's concepts of "semiotic" and "negativity," which resonate with other terms such as "Nepantla" and "Interspace." These works suggest that an epistemological argument for a fundamental gender difference is that our *bodies* are decoding devices which provide context for language. Might critical analysis based in this theory disclose a method to re-balance the definitions and canons of literature? This theory is worth further examination.

My 'public acts' include a weekly extemporaneous woman's writing group and a weekly radio show *Songs-Voices-Poems* for public radio station KRFY. Through these activities, I nurture the notion that women offer different and valuable perspectives. Perspectives which have been ignored, suppressed and undermined throughout history, such as those of Maria Edgeworth, Emily Lawless, and Else Jerusalem. The basic question for my work is therefore whether it is possible to create a mythology, as described powerfully during Laird Hunt's classes, rooted in the echoes of women's voices.

Appendix: Root Songs, Poems and Readings

Bishop, Elizabeth.   "A Miracle for Breakfast," "One Art"

Brel, Jacques.   "La Chanson des Vieux Amants"

Cummings, Edward Estlin.   "Somewhere I have never travelled"

Dickinson, Emily.   "I dwell in Possibility," "I heard, as if I had no Ear"

Eliot, T.S.   *The Waste Land*

Henley, William Earnest.   "Invictus"

Kimmerer, Robin Wall.   *Braiding Sweetgrass: Indigenous Wisdom, Scientific Knowledge and the Teachings of Plants*

Paley, Grace.   "Here"

Siegel, Daniel J. Siegel.   *The Mind: A Journey to the Soul of Being Human*

Stein, Gertrude.   "Would he like it if I told him: A Complete Portrait of Picasso," "Matisse," *Tender Buttons*

Whitman, Walt.   *Song of Myself*

Rerooted   127

Jackie Henrion

Rerooted

51956521R00080

Made in the USA
Lexington, KY
07 September 2019